SEVEN
A MAXIMUM
HIGH

Getting Better   6

Magic Streets   18

Where Have You Been Tonight?   24

Going For Gold   13

On Standby   30

Out By My Side   36

Lies   39

This Day Was Ours   46

Ladyman   51

Falling From The Sky   56

Bully Boy   62

Parallel Lines   66

POLYGRAM MUSIC PUBLISHING LIMITED

GETTING BETTER

You are my guiding light
And you're shining brighter
You shine like Tokyo
It's getting better all the time
And the hills are alive
With the sound of music
It's getting better all the time

It's getting better all the time
I've got my wings and I can fly
I will fly to you
You are my one ambition
Show me your recognition
It's getting better all the time

A nod's as good as a wink
No matter what you're thinking
You are the missing link
It's getting better all the time
And the streets are alive
With the sound of music
It's getting better all the time
I could take you to work
And show you some of my perks
It's getting better all the time

MAGIC STREETS

We went to the darkest side of town
Where all the ladies hang around
And all the loving can be found, in town
We went to the Early Learning Centre
With the money that I've lent yer
It's the price of an education
Won't you spur me on

To find a place to meet
And I'll hit you with the worth
I've been down magic streets
Because I'm as big as the universe
This could never last forever
Because you can't fix what's left in bits
And all your magic tricks are magic

Will you have another one in there
And toast the fact that I'm so rare
And boast about how I don't care, because I'm
there
So put your anorak on
And go out and find yourself some fun
It's the price of an education
Won't you spur me on

So put your hooded cloak on
And go out and buy yourself some fun
Won't you spur me on

Streets are paved with people
And you're just another one

WHERE HAVE YOU BEEN TONIGHT?

There is nothing to do
And nowhere to go when you need to
I took to you
I took to you, from you I drew
Nothing but a lonely smile
I wanna go out in the sun
But there isn't any sun
And I want the sun
I wanna change the way I look
Because I haven't any luck
And my brain is tired
Where have you been?
If you hold me back I'll kick you in the shins
Until your night's on fire
It's good to be alive
Where have you been tonight?
With the last cries of night
Yes we'll see

There is nothing to prove
Because no-one can lose
But you will do
I took to you
I took to you, from you I drew
Nothing but a lonely smile
I wanna go out in the sun
But there isn't any sun
And I want the sun
I wanna change the way I look
Because I haven't any luck
And my brain is tired
What have you seen?
If you stop me now
I'll push you until you scream
Until your night's on fire
It's good to be alive
Where have you been tonight?
With the last cries of life
Yes, you'll soon feel the knife
With the last cries of life
Yes we'll see

GOING FOR GOLD

I never said never, ever
You took the words right out of my mouth
Is the sea your sunshine
Have you been told
The sea is your life-line
You're going for gold
You took the words right out of my mouth

Time and time and time again
I look to me my only friend
Time and time and time again
Are you here for my pleasure
Or are you going for gold
Are you going for gold

I never said never, ever
You took the shine right out of my smile
Is the moon your night time
Have you been sold
The moon is your life-line
You're going for gold
You took the shine right out of my smile

While my mind is blind again
I look to me my only friend
Time and time and time again
Are you here for my pleasure
Or are you going for gold
Are you going for gold

ON STANDBY

Would you stay on standby
Because I need another alibi
In the wrong place at the wrong time
Could you talk a fine rhyme
I need to know that I'll be fine
Bulletproof

It's like I've never been born
We conceive in the alleyways
It's like I've never been born
We believe in other ways
That you do, and you did
And there's proof that we did wrong tonight

Could you sense a tragedy
Because I saw it on the BBC
There's a panel on that channel
Could you walk a narrow line
I need to know I'll serve my time
With some use

It's like I've never been born
We conceive in the alleyways
It's like I've never been born
We believe in other ways
That you do, and you did
And there's proof that we did wrong tonight

And tonight, you can cry if you want to
But it won't help you
You can cry, if you want to
But it won't help you
To get through this crime
It will plague you, standby

We did wrong, we did wrong

OUT BY MY SIDE

When will you come outside
Where do you think you can hide
And when the sun turns to night
You keep your curtains shut tight

Where is the trust in yourself
I don't have claims on your wealth anymore
How can you stay locked inside
You should be out by my side

How do you think you'll survive
When will you learn you're alive
And when the wind blows, you're mine
I've made your door my shrine

Where is the trust in yourself
I don't have claims on your wealth anymore
How can you stay locked inside
You should be out by my side

How can you stay locked inside
You should be out by my side

How can you stay locked inside
You should be out as my bride

LIES

I know tomorrow won't be the same
I've seen the future and I saw who's to blame
Left nothing here for me
I've seen the future but I can't see you
I've seen through

Everything that you said, I could say you're a liar
Everything that you do, I could say you could try
A little bit
She's been lying, now you're trying
But you're gonna find no way out tonight

Everyday will be like the last
Who are you to think it will pass
Take care of everything
I've seen the future but I can't see you
I've seen through

Everything that you said, I could say you're a liar
Everything that you do, I could say you could try
A little bit
She's been lying, now you're trying
But you're gonna find no way out tonight

I've got this feeling
That it won't last the night

THIS DAY WAS OURS

This day was ours
But you stay for hours everytime
But you won't be mine
It must be good in Hollywood
You laugh, you walk, you scream
You're in the dark all the time
Can I say you're in your prime

Now I will sing, of that I must be king
I'm in the dark all the time
Of that I must be king
Now we can fly away
The stars are burning bright in the night

You're in demand
I've got plans to make you understand
But you won't be mine
I could trace the very place
You were before
And where you will next be
You mean the world to me

This day was ours
You've got powers of a different kind
Can I say you're in your prime

LADYMAN

I'm a lady, I'm a man
Try to do the best I possibly
Can you feel it, feel alive
Never had a feeling in my life
Until tomorrow
I'm afraid you're wasting your time

Should you prove to yourself
That you're nobody else
It throws me everytime
Lay me aside, I'd die for my pride
My bones are buried alive

I'm amazing, I can breathe
Trying to find out more but I can't
Read the answers, re-write my life
Re-write the times
Until tomorrow
I'm afraid you're wasting your time

Should you prove to yourself
That you're nobody else
It throws me everytime
Lay me aside, I'd die for my pride
My bones are buried alive
My heart is broken glass in a plastercast
It throws me everytime
I've found my place at last behind this mask
But I'm afraid you're wasting your time

FALLING FROM THE SKY

I can't speak
And I need to tell you how it feels
I get weak
When I try to start the day without the rain
It's no fun
When I try to offer you the sun
It's too high
Will you try to shake your pride or stay inside
and hide

Can you feel it falling with the rain
You see through diamonds in your eyes
Falling from the sky
You walk on water everytime
Falling from the sky

I need sleep
But I'll try to keep myself on my feet
And that's sweet
Could you try to lose yourself in someone else
It's no fun
When I try to offer you the sun
And I'm wired
Could you try to shake your pride or stay inside
and hide

Can you feel it falling with the rain
You see through diamonds in your eyes
Falling from the sky
Can you feel it falling with the rain
You walk on water everytime
Falling from the sky
You bathe in beauty everytime
Falling from the sky
Falling from the sky

BULLY BOY

You knocked me off my feet
And I fell face first on the concrete
I took a blow to the limbs
I didn't even know him

There's no point in hiding
The hate you confide in
The pain that you call your own
There's no point in shying
From fists that are flying
The boy is on his own

You looked me in the eye
I bet you thought I was paralysed
I took a blow to the chest
Now I've been underestimated

There's no point in hiding
The hate you confide in
The pain that you call your own
There's no point in shying
From fists that are flying
The boy is on his own

I'll fight you to the death
I'll fight you to the death

PARALLEL LINES

Suck on this
Doing the bits
Topping the hits
I've walked miles to be with you
Listen to me
On my hands and knees
Feeding my greed
And all the while I think it's true
It's a maximum high, with my parallel lines

The mirror is long
It's a way to belong
And it's keeping me strong
And all the style is showing through
It's one day of trust
Three years of lust
And it's my life or bust
And all the while I think it's true
It's a maximum high, with my parallel lines

You're my queen
And you're my machine
A fine dream team
I'm feeling bright, I feel all new
Yes that was a joke
Everytime that you spoke
Until you finally choked
And I'll rule my own roost
It's a maximum high, with my parallel lines

I could fax you at work
And pick you up in my Merc
And dig deep in your dirt
It's the in thing to do
So suck on this
And I'm making my lists
And I'm topping the hits
I've walked miles to be with you
It's a maximum high, with my parallel lines
Shaking off me

You're a millionaire
And you've been everywhere
And you've done every dare
Can you see my point of view
And it looks like you know
Where you're going to go
Where you'll blow all your dough
And all the while I think it's true
It's a maximum high, with my parallel lines
Shaking off me
It's my whirlwind, and it's my last fling

It's the devil in me
And I won't set it free
'Cause it's locked in me
And all the style is showing through
It's my honeymoon
I'll take it this afternoon
Egg and spoon to the moon
I'm feeling bright, I feel all new
It's a maximum high, with my parallel lines
Shaking off me
It's my whirlwind, and it's my last fling
Shaking off me
Now I know it's time, for a maximum high
Shaking off me

Getting better
Getting better
Getting better

GETTING BETTER

Words & Music by Thomas Gladwin, Rick Witter, Alan Leach & Paul Banks

you shine— like To - ky - o,———— it's get - ting bet - ter all the

time.———————

(Verses 2 & 3 see block lyric)

And the hills are a -

live with the sound of mu - sic, it's get - ting bet - ter all the

time.—————

7

it's get-ting bet - ter all ___ the time. ___

It's get-ting bet -

- ter.

10

Verse 2:
A nod's as good as a wink
No matter what you're thinking,
You are the missing link,
It's getting better all the time.

And the streets are alive
With the sound of music,
It's getting better all the time.

*Verse 3:(**D.%.**)*
I could take you to work
And show you some of my perks,
It's getting better all the time.

GOING FOR GOLD

Words & Music by Thomas Gladwin, Rick Witter, Alan Leach & Paul Banks

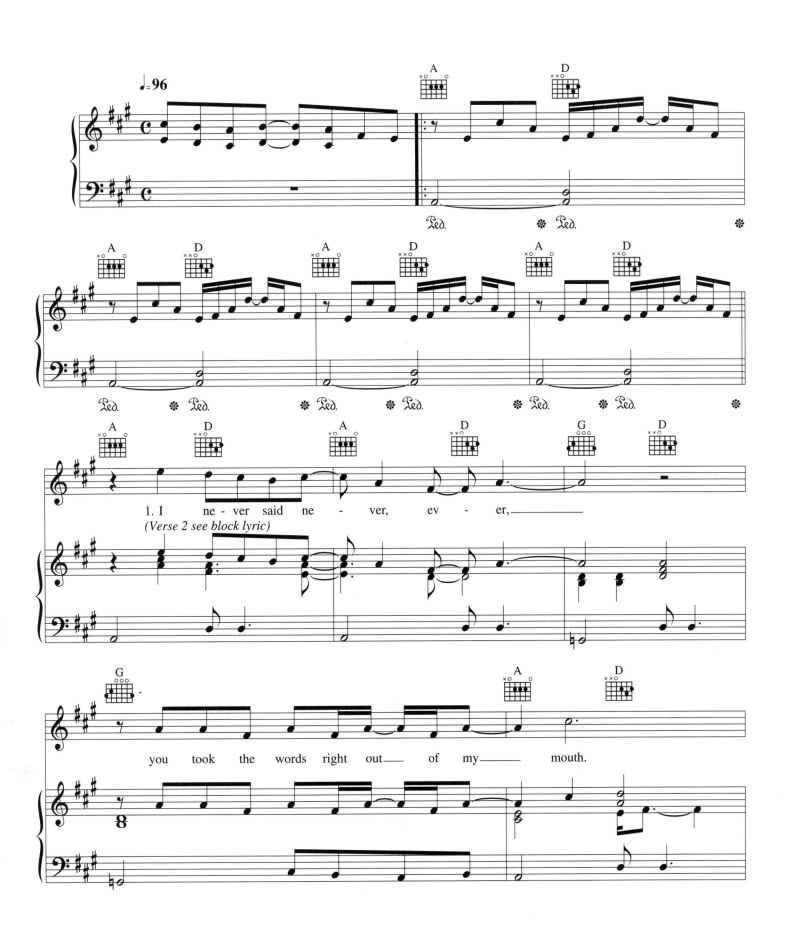

I look to me, my on - ly friend.

Time and time and time a - gain,_____ are you here for my plea -

- sure,_____ or are you go - ing for gold,_____

are you go - ing for gold?_____

Verse 2:
I never said never ever,
You took the shine right out of my smile.
Is the moon your night time,
The moon is your lifeline,
Going for gold,
You took the shine right out of my smile.

MAGIC STREETS

Words & Music by Thomas Gladwin, Rick Witter, Alan Leach & Paul Banks

Verse 2:

Will you have another one in there
And toast the fact that I'm so rare,
And boast about how I don't care, because I'm there.
So put your anorak on
And go out and find yourself some fun.
Won't you spur me on…

Verse 3: (D.𝄋.)

So put your hooded cloak on
And go out and buy yourself some fun.
Won't you spur me on…

WHERE HAVE YOU BEEN TONIGHT?

Words & Music by Thomas Gladwin, Rick Witter, Alan Leach & Paul Banks

There is noth-ing to do,___ and no-where to go when you need___

to. ____ I took to you, I took to you, from you I drew

no - thing but a lone - ly smile. ____ I

wan - na go out in the sun, ____ but there is - n't an - y

sun, and I want the sun. ____ I wan - na change the way I look, ____

you   been   to-night?—   With   the   last——   cries   of   night,—

—   yes   we'll—   see.

—   yes   we'll——   see.

Where have you been to-night?— With the last—

— cries of life.— Yes, you'll soon feel the knife..

— With the last——— cries of life,— yes we'll see.

28

Verse 2:
There is nothing to prove
Because no one can lose,
But you will do.
I took to you,
I took to you, from you I drew
Nothing but a lonely smile.
I wanna go out in the sun,
But there isn't any sun.
I wanna change the way I look,
Because I haven't any luck
And my brain is tired.
What have you seen?
If you stop me now
I'll push you till you scream,
Until your night's on fire.
It's good to be alive.
Where have you been tonight?
With the last cries of life,
Yes we'll see.

ON STANDBY

Words & Music by Thomas Gladwin, Rick Witter, Alan Leach & Paul Banks

It's like I've ne-ver been born, we be-lieve in oth-er ways that you do, and you did, and there's proof that we did wrong to-night.

To Coda ⊕ 1.

⊕ *Coda*

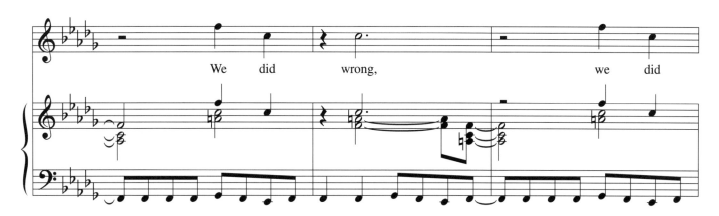

We did wrong, we did

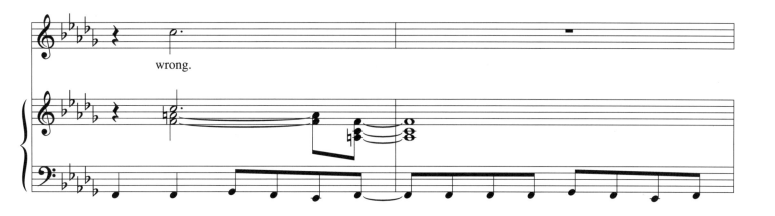

wrong.

Verse 2:
Could you sense a tragedy?
Because I saw it on the BBC,
There's a panel on that channel.
Could you walk a narrow line?
I need to know I'll serve my time
With some use.

OUT BY MY SIDE

Words & Music by Thomas Gladwin, Rick Witter, Alan Leach & Paul Banks

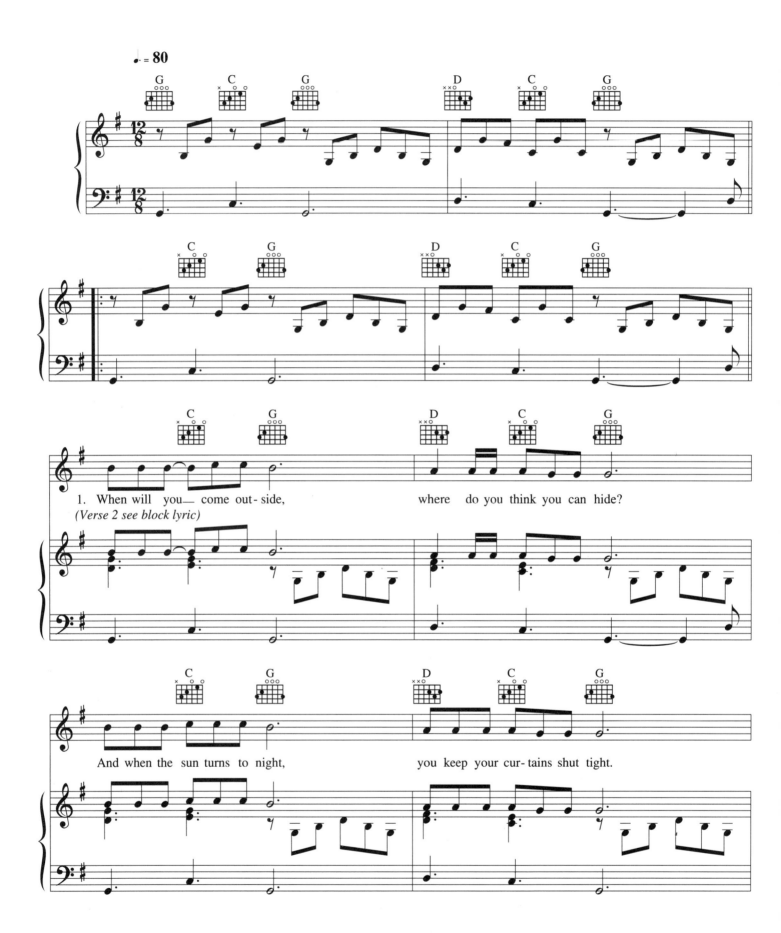

1. When will you come out-side, where do you think you can hide?
(Verse 2 see block lyric)

And when the sun turns to night, you keep your cur-tains shut tight.

You should be out by my side.————
You should be out as my bride.————

Verse 2:
How do you think you'll survive,
When will you learn you're alive?
And when the wind blows, you're mine,
I've made your door my shrine.

LIES

Words & Music by Thomas Gladwin, Rick Witter, Alan Leach & Paul Banks

1. I know to-mor-row won't be the same,—
(Verse 2 see block lyric)

—— I've seen the fu - ture and I saw who's to blame.— left noth-ing here—

—— for me, I've seen the fu - ture but I can't see

more.

She's been ly - ing and now____ you're try - ing but you're

gon - na find a way out to - night.____

She's been ly - ing and now____ you're try - ing but you're

Verse 2:
Every day will be like the last,
Who are you to think it will pass?
Take care of everything,
I've seen the future but I can't see you,
I've seen through.

THIS DAY WAS OURS

Words & Music by Thomas Gladwin, Rick Witter, Alan Leach & Paul Banks

Of that I must be____ king.

49

Verse 2:
You're in demand,
I've got plans to make you understand,
But you won't be mine.
I could trace the very place you were before
And where you will next be,
You mean the world to me.

Verse 3: (D.%.)
This day was ours,
You've got the powers of a different kind,
Can I say you're in your prime?

LADYMAN

Words & Music by Thomas Gladwin, Rick Witter, Alan Leach & Paul Banks

Verse 2:
I'm amazing, I can breathe,
Trying to find out more,
But I can't read the answers, re-write my life.
Re-write the times
Until tomorrow,
I'm afraid you're wasting your time.

FALLING FROM THE SKY

Words & Music by Thomas Gladwin, Rick Witter, Alan Leach & Paul Banks

Can you feel it fall-ing with— the rain?—
{ You see__ through dia-
{ You walk__ on wa-

-monds in__ your eyes,__ }
-ter ev-'ry time,__ } fall-ing from— the sky.—

1. N.C.

__ You bathe__ in beau-

2.

Verse 2:
I need sleep,
But I'll try to keep myself on my feet,
And that's sweet,
Could you try to lose yourself in someone else?
It's no fun
When I try to offer you the sun,
And I'm wired,
Could you try to shake your pride or stay inside and hide?

BULLY BOY

Words & Music by Thomas Gladwin, Rick Witter, Alan Leach & Paul Banks

1. You

Verse 2.
You looked me in the eyes,
I bet you thought I was paralysed.
I took a blow to the chest,
Now I've been underestimated.

PARALLEL LINES

Words & Music by Thomas Gladwin, Rick Witter, Alan Leach & Paul Banks

5. You're a mil-li-on-aire, and you've been ev-'ry-where, and you've done ev-'ry dare,
(Verse 6 see block lyric)

can you see my point of view? And it looks like you know

where you're go-ing to go, where you'll blow all your dough,

and all the while I think it's true. It's a max-i-mum high,

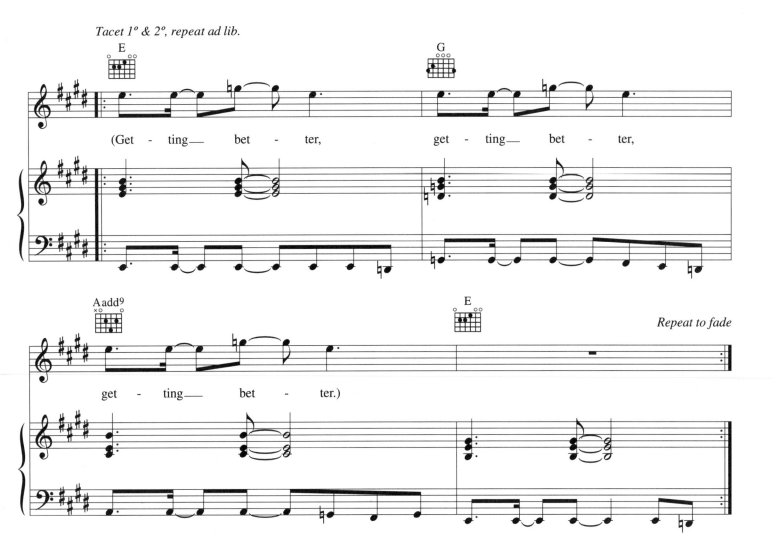

Verse 2:
The mirror is long,
It's a way to belong,
And it's keeping me strong,
And all the style is showing through.
It's one day of trust,
Three years of lust,
And it's my life or bust,
And all the while I think it's true.
It's a maximum high, with my parallel lines.

Verse 3:
You're my queen,
And you're my machine,
A fine dream team,
I'm feeling bright, I feel all new.
Yes, that was a joke,
Everytime that you spoke,
Until you finally choked,
And I'll rule my own roost.
It's a maximum high, with my parallel lines.

Verse 4:
I could fax you at work,
And pick you up in my Merc,
And dig deep in your dirt,
It's the in thing to do.
So suck on this,
And I'm making my lists,
And I'm topping the hits,
I've walked miles just to be with you.
It's a maximum high, with my parallel lines.
Shaking off me.

Verse 6:
It's the devil in me,
And I won't set it free,
'Cause it's locked in me,
And all the style is showing through.
It's my honeymoon,
I'll take it this afternoon,
Egg and spoon to the moon,
I'm feeling bright, I feel all new.
It's a maximum high, with my parallel lines.
Shaking off me.
Now I know it's time for a maximum high.
Shaking off me.

Exclusive Distributors:

Music Sales Limited
8/9 Frith Street, London W1V 5TZ, England

Music Sales Pty Limited
120 Rothschild Avenue, Rosebery, NSW 2018, Australia

Order No. AM939191
ISBN 0-7119-5972-2
This book © Copyright 1996 by PolyGram Music Publishing Limited
Visit the Internet Music Shop at
http://www.musicsales.co.uk

Book design by Michael Bell Design
Music arranged by Roger Day
Music processed by Paul Ewers Music Design

Your Guarantee of Quality:

As publishers, we strive to produce every book to the highest commercial standards

The music has been freshly engraved and, whilst endeavouring to retain the
original running order of the recorded album, the book has been carefully designed to
minimise awkward page turns and to make playing from it a real pleasure

Particular care has been given to specifying acid-free, neutral-sized
paper made from pulps which have not been elemental chlorine bleached

This pulp is from farmed sustainable forests and was produced with special regard for the environment

Throughout, the printing and binding have been planned to ensure
a sturdy, attractive publication which should give years of enjoyment

If your copy fails to meet our high standards, please inform us and we will gladly replace it

Music Sales' complete catalogue describes thousands of titles and
is available in full colour sections by subject, direct from Music Sales Limited
Please state your areas of interest and send a cheque/postal order for £1.50 for postage to:
Music Sales Limited, Newmarket Road, Bury St. Edmunds, Suffolk IP33 3YB

Printed in the United Kingdom by
Halstan & Co Limited, Amersham, Buckinghamshire.